S0-AGA-322

COOL BOOK of seek & find

Kidsbooks®

Copyright © 2017 Kidsbooks, LLC
3535 West Peterson Avenue
Chicago, IL 60659

All rights reserved, including the right
of reproduction in whole or in part in any form.

Search & Find is a registered trademark of Kidsbooks, LLC.

Printed in China
111701002GD

Visit us at **www.kidsbooks.com**

LOOK FOR LISA

WHERE ARE THEY?

Look for Lisa in all sorts of crazy places!
While you're looking,
you'll see crazy things, such as:

- Hippos at a rock concert
- Cactuses on the beach
- Parrots in the library
- Surfers on a farm
- Frogs at the flea market
- Snow White at the marathon
- Unicorns in Utah

. . . and much, much more!

Look for **Lisa** at the
Marathon
and...

- [ ] Angel
- [ ] Barrel
- [ ] Basketball
- [ ] Bucket
- [ ] Cane
- [ ] Chef
- [ ] Cowboy
- [ ] Deer
- [ ] Diving board
- [ ] Doctor
- [ ] Elephants (2)
- [ ] Ice-cream cone
- [ ] Kite
- [ ] Motorcycle
- [ ] Musical notes (3)
- [ ] Net
- [ ] Octopus
- [ ] Periscope
- [ ] Policeman
- [ ] Rocket
- [ ] Roller skates
- [ ] Sad face
- [ ] Scooter
- [ ] "Shortcut"
- [ ] Sombrero
- [ ] Speed skater
- [ ] Spotted dog
- [ ] Strongman
- [ ] Surfer
- [ ] Taxi
- [ ] Tuba
- [ ] Umbrella

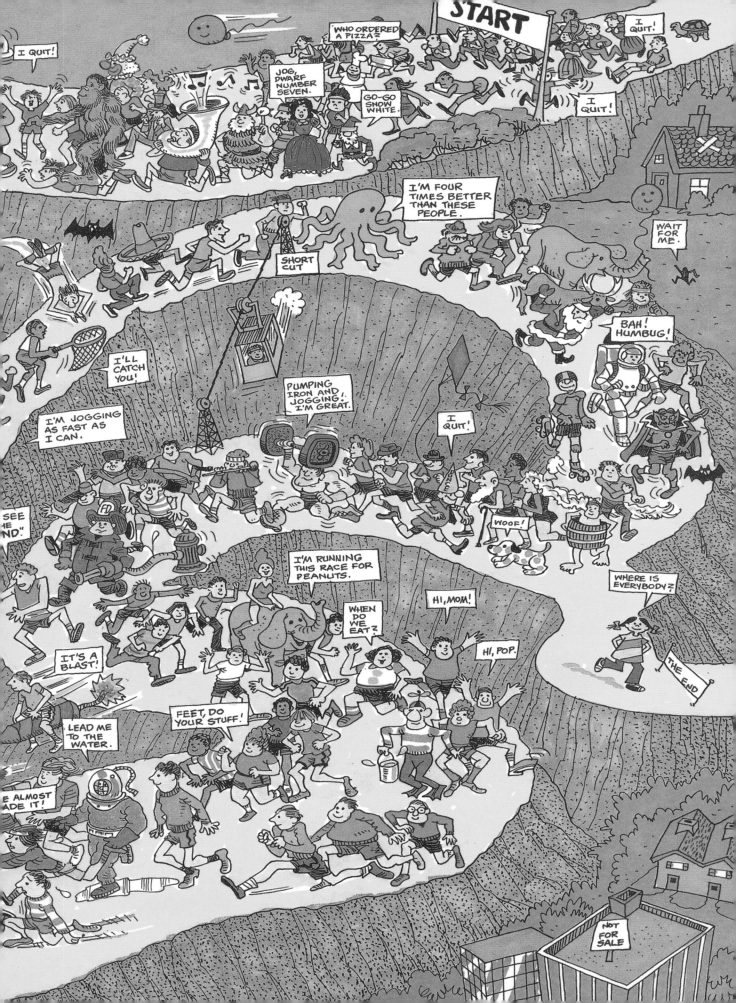

Look for Lisa
After School
and...

- ☐ Balloon
- ☐ Basketballs (2)
- ☐ Baton
- ☐ Bird
- ☐ Camera
- ☐ Chimney
- ☐ Clock faces (2)
- ☐ Donkey
- ☐ Elephant
- ☐ Fish with a hat
- ☐ Flower
- ☐ Grocery cart
- ☐ Hat with propeller
- ☐ Huck Finn
- ☐ Igloo
- ☐ Paper hat
- ☐ Parrot
- ☐ Pencil
- ☐ Pig
- ☐ Plane
- ☐ Rabbit
- ☐ Robot
- ☐ Sailor
- ☐ Ski jumper
- ☐ Smelly potion
- ☐ Snowman
- ☐ Stool
- ☐ Sunglasses
- ☐ Turtle
- ☐ Unicorn
- ☐ Viking helmet

Look for Lisa at the Rock Concert and...

- ☐ Alien
- ☐ Balloons (6)
- ☐ Barbell
- ☐ Bowling ball
- ☐ Crown
- ☐ Doctor
- ☐ Fish tank
- ☐ Flamingo
- ☐ Flowers
- ☐ Hot-dog stand
- ☐ Knight
- ☐ Lamppost
- ☐ Masked man
- ☐ Moon
- ☐ Mummy
- ☐ Net
- ☐ Painter
- ☐ Prisoner
- ☐ Rabbit
- ☐ Snowman
- ☐ Stack of pizza boxes
- ☐ Stars (6)
- ☐ Tin Man
- ☐ Tombstones (2)
- ☐ Trampoline
- ☐ Viking
- ☐ Waiter
- ☐ Witch
- ☐ Zebra

Look for **Lisa** on the **Farm** and...

- [ ] Cactus
- [ ] Cave
- [ ] Clouds (3)
- [ ] Donkey
- [ ] "Don't Stop" sign
- [ ] Egg
- [ ] Elephant
- [ ] Eskimo
- [ ] Finish line
- [ ] Fox
- [ ] Ghost
- [ ] Giant pumpkin
- [ ] "Grade A"
- [ ] Horses (3)
- [ ] Lion
- [ ] Log pile
- [ ] Message in a bottle
- [ ] Net
- [ ] Periscope
- [ ] Pitchfork
- [ ] Policeman
- [ ] Prisoner
- [ ] Rowboat
- [ ] Scuba diver
- [ ] Stop sign
- [ ] "Summer"
- [ ] Surfboards (2)
- [ ] Tent
- [ ] Turkey
- [ ] Water bucket
- [ ] Weather vane

Look for Lisa at the Beach and...

- ☐ Artist
- ☐ Beach ball
- ☐ Broom
- ☐ Bunch of balloons
- ☐ Cactus (4)
- ☐ Castle
- ☐ Cello
- ☐ Crocodile
- ☐ Cruise ship
- ☐ Diving board
- ☐ Hearts (3)
- ☐ Horse
- ☐ Jack-in-the-box
- ☐ Kite
- ☐ Lifeguard
- ☐ Lost swim trunks
- ☐ Magnifying glass
- ☐ Merman
- ☐ Palm trees (3)
- ☐ Pickle barrel
- ☐ Policeman
- ☐ Sailboat
- ☐ Sailors (2)
- ☐ Sea serpent
- ☐ Seahorse
- ☐ Starfish (9)
- ☐ Swans (2)
- ☐ Telescope
- ☐ Trash can
- ☐ Tricycle
- ☐ Turtle
- ☐ Whale

Look for Lisa at the
Big Sale
and...

- ☐ Balloon
- ☐ Clothespins (9)
- ☐ Count Dracula
- ☐ Disappearing men (2)
- ☐ "Don't Stop Shopping"
- ☐ Flower hat
- ☐ Football
- ☐ Football helmet
- ☐ Gumball machine
- ☐ Hard hat
- ☐ Janitor
- ☐ Kite
- ☐ Magic mirror
- ☐ Manhole cover
- ☐ Octopus
- ☐ Paint can
- ☐ Paper airplane
- ☐ Pig
- ☐ Pogo stick
- ☐ Polka-dot shorts
- ☐ Rabbit
- ☐ Rain slicker
- ☐ Rat
- ☐ Robot
- ☐ Roller skates
- ☐ Shirtless shopper
- ☐ Ski jump
- ☐ Skis (8)
- ☐ Teddy bear
- ☐ Turtle

Look for **Lisa** around the **World** and...

- [ ] Airplane
- [ ] Castle
- [ ] Cruise ship
- [ ] Elephant
- [ ] Fisherman
- [ ] Flamingo
- [ ] Foot
- [ ] Golf club
- [ ] Guitar
- [ ] Horse
- [ ] Hot-air balloon
- [ ] Ladder
- [ ] Lighthouse
- [ ] Lion
- [ ] Movie camera
- [ ] Penguins (6)
- [ ] Pine trees (6)
- [ ] Pizza man
- [ ] Refrigerator
- [ ] Sailboats (4)
- [ ] Santa Claus
- [ ] Scarves (2)
- [ ] Seal
- [ ] Sea monster
- [ ] Skis (8)
- [ ] Sombrero
- [ ] Submarine
- [ ] Surfboards (3)
- [ ] Television
- [ ] UFOs (2)
- [ ] Walrus
- [ ] Whale

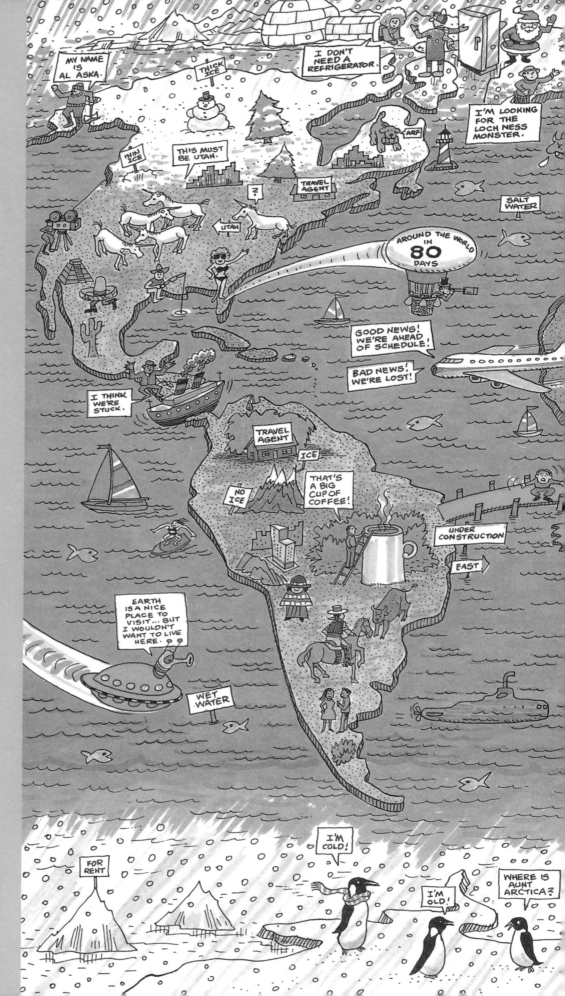

Look for **Lisa** at the **Library** and...

- [ ] Baseball
- [ ] Birdcage
- [ ] Bowling pins (10)
- [ ] Brooms (2)
- [ ] Cactus
- [ ] Cactus book
- [ ] Cake
- [ ] Campfire
- [ ] Candle
- [ ] Car
- [ ] Football player
- [ ] Frying pan
- [ ] Globe
- [ ] Hamburger
- [ ] Hearts (4)
- [ ] Hockey stick
- [ ] Hot dog
- [ ] Jack-in-the-box
- [ ] Knight
- [ ] Monster hands (3)
- [ ] Musical note
- [ ] Napoleon
- [ ] Old tire
- [ ] Pole-vaulter
- [ ] Policewoman
- [ ] "Quiet" signs (6)
- [ ] Smiley face
- [ ] Teapot
- [ ] Trap door
- [ ] Tricycle
- [ ] Wagon
- [ ] Witch

Look for **Lisa** at the **Amusement Park** and...

- [ ] All-north weather vane
- [ ] Archer
- [ ] Cheese
- [ ] Clock
- [ ] Clowns (3)
- [ ] Cowboys (2)
- [ ] Crocodile
- [ ] Crooked chimney
- [ ] Diving board
- [ ] Dollar sign
- [ ] Fishing pole
- [ ] Heads without bodies (2)
- [ ] Ice block
- [ ] Manhole
- [ ] Moon
- [ ] Mouse hole
- [ ] Mummy
- [ ] Pear
- [ ] Snowman
- [ ] Space explorer
- [ ] Tent
- [ ] Tied-up man
- [ ] Tin Man
- [ ] Tombstones (3)
- [ ] "Tunnel of Love"
- [ ] Umbrella
- [ ] Witch
- [ ] Wristwatches (7)

Look for **Lisa** at the **Flea Market** and...

- [ ] Birdcages (2)
- [ ] Clown doll
- [ ] Court jester
- [ ] Cowboy hat
- [ ] Crown
- [ ] Elephant
- [ ] Elf
- [ ] Fish (3)
- [ ] Fishing hook
- [ ] "Flea Market Map"
- [ ] Football
- [ ] Golf club
- [ ] Graduate
- [ ] Horse
- [ ] Monster hand
- [ ] Necklace
- [ ] Old tire
- [ ] Paintbrush
- [ ] Pear
- [ ] Records (8)
- [ ] Saddle
- [ ] Sailor hat
- [ ] Scuba diver
- [ ] Shopping bag
- [ ] Skateboard
- [ ] Telephone booth
- [ ] Train conductor
- [ ] Trumpet
- [ ] Wheelbarrow
- [ ] Witch

Look for Lisa as the
Circus
Comes to
Town
and...

Look for **Lisa** in
Prehistoric Times
and...

- [ ] Baby carriage
- [ ] Candle
- [ ] Cherry
- [ ] Clothespin
- [ ] Dinosaur egg
- [ ] Faucet
- [ ] Four-leaf clover
- [ ] Hammer
- [ ] Hot chocolate
- [ ] Life preserver
- [ ] Message in a bottle
- [ ] Necklace
- [ ] Necktie
- [ ] "No U Turn"
- [ ] Palm trees (2)
- [ ] Periscope
- [ ] Piggy bank
- [ ] Pizza
- [ ] Ring
- [ ] Scarecrow
- [ ] Skateboard
- [ ] Stars (2)
- [ ] Swimming duck
- [ ] Tire
- [ ] Toothbrush
- [ ] Volcanoes (2)
- [ ] Wooden wheel

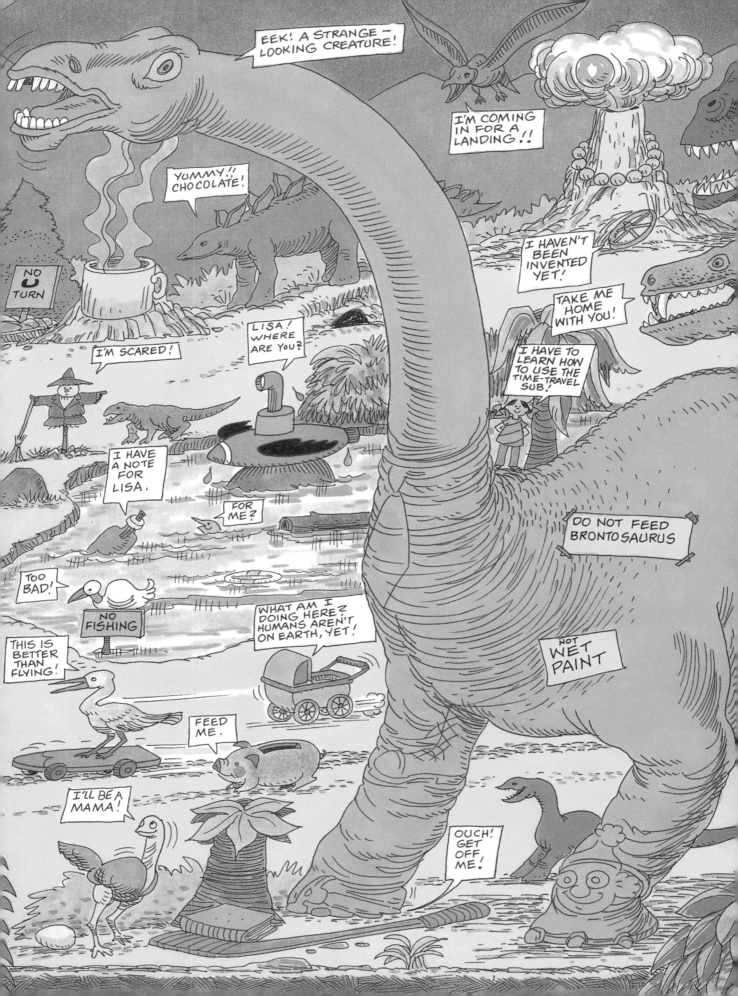

Look for Lisa in the **Creepy Castle** and...

- [ ] Apples (2)
- [ ] Arrow
- [ ] Ball and chain
- [ ] Balloon
- [ ] Banana peel
- [ ] Baseball cap
- [ ] Birdcage
- [ ] Bones (6)
- [ ] Bowling pin
- [ ] Broom
- [ ] Calendar
- [ ] Carrot
- [ ] Crayon
- [ ] Door knocker
- [ ] Flying bats (3)
- [ ] Football
- [ ] Ghost
- [ ] Jar
- [ ] Lantern
- [ ] Mice (5)
- [ ] Nail
- [ ] Oil can
- [ ] Paintbrush
- [ ] Pencil
- [ ] Rose
- [ ] Scissors
- [ ] Wristwatch
- [ ] Yo-yo

Look for **Lisa** as she **Rocks and Rolls** and...

Look for Lisa and...

Baseball bat	Cane	Moon	Sun
Bird	Fire hydrant	Octopus	Tire
Bottle	Fish	Rabbit	Top hat
Broom	Flowers (2)	Saw	Turtle
Cactus	Hammers (2)	Scarves (2)	Wreath
Can	Kite	Snake	